A Teddy Horsley Book

The Pre

C000182537

Teddy Horsley meets the Wise Men
Based on Matthew 2

by Leslie J Francis and Nicola M Slee
Pictures by Ferelith Eccles Williams

The Bear facts:

The Teddy Horsley Bible Series is designed to build bridges between the young child's day to day experiences of the world and major biblical themes and stories.

Both authors work in church-related institutions of education. Nicola Slee is Director of Studies at the Aston Training Scheme in Birmingham. Leslie Francis is Professor of Pastoral Theology at the University of Wales, Lampeter, and Trinity College, Carmarthen. The illustrator, Laura Cooper, is a teacher and artist.

The Teddy Horsley Series is a result of extensive research into the religious development of young children, and the authors' and illustrator's wide experience of educational work in schools and churches.

Published by:
National Christian Education Council
1020 Bristol Road
Selly Oak
Birmingham B29 6LB

British Library Cataloguing in Publication Data:
A catalogue record for this book is available from the British Library.
Text © Leslie J Francis and Nicola M Slee 1985
Illustrations © National Christian Education Council 1994

First published 1985 by Collins, London
ISBN 0-7197-0842-7

Reprinted 1990, 1994, 1997
Printed in England

Teddy Horsley is a bear who likes choosing presents.

Before Christmas Teddy Horsley goes shopping

with Mr and Mrs Henry, Lucy, Walter and Betsy Bear.

He chooses a kite for Lucy and Walter,

a pot plant for
Mrs Henry,

and chocolates for
Mr Henry.

He wraps the presents in colourful paper

and ties them with bright ribbon.

Teddy Horsley places his presents around the Christmas tree.

Teddy Horsley is a bear who likes opening presents.

On Christmas day Teddy Horsley comes to the tree

with Mr and Mrs Henry, Lucy, Walter and Betsy Bear.

He unwraps a space suit from Mr and Mrs Henry,

boots from Lucy, and a helmet from Walter.

Teddy Horsley dresses up in his presents.

Teddy Horsley is a bear who likes giving presents.

After Christmas Teddy Horsley takes a present to church

with Mr and Mrs Henry, Lucy, Walter and Betsy Bear.

He sees the wise men bring gifts to the crib.

He touches the gleaming cup of gold.

He sniffs the sweet smell of the frankincense.

He puts his paw in the jar of myrrh.

Teddy Horsley gives his present to the infant Jesus.

In *The Present*, Teddy Horsley's choosing, giving, and receiving of gifts at Christmas helps him to share in the wise men's presentation of gifts to the infant Jesus.

Jesus was born in the town of Bethlehem in Judaea, during the time when Herod was king. Soon afterwards, some men who studied the stars came from the east to Jerusalem and asked, "Where is the baby born to be the king of the Jews? We saw his star when it came up in the east, and we have come to worship him" . . . And on their way they saw the same star they had seen in the east. When they saw it, how happy they were, what joy was theirs! It went ahead of them until it stopped over the place where the child was. They went into the house, and when they saw the child with his mother Mary, they knelt down and worshipped him. They brought out their gifts of gold, frankincense, and myrrh, and presented them to him.

Matthew 2.1-2,9-11

The following questions suggest further ways of developing the links between the young child's experience, the story, and the Bible passage.

Talk about Christmas presents:
Do you give presents at Christmas? Who to?
Why do you give presents to them?
What would you like to choose for them?
Who gives presents to you at Christmas?
Why do they give you presents?
What would you like them to choose for you?

Talk about the story:
What presents did Teddy Horsley choose before Christmas?
What presents did Teddy Horsley open on Christmas Day?
What did Teddy Horsley see in church?
Who brought presents to the infant Jesus?
What did they bring?

Think some more about the story:
What other presents might Teddy Horsley choose for his family?
What other presents might Teddy Horsley like to open on
Christmas Day?
What present do you think Teddy Horsley took to church?
What presents do you think the others brought to church?

Think about the Bible passage:

Why did the wise men bring gifts to Jesus?
How did they feel when they found Jesus and gave him their presents?
How do people give presents to Jesus today?
What presents would Jesus want people to give him today?
What present might you bring to Jesus?

Titles in the series

Other publications to help young children explore the Bible:

Bible Storytime

Six books each containing twenty Bible stories from the Old and New Testaments, retold for the under sevens with related activities and prayer ideas.

Friezes

With clear, bold outlines for easy colouring and cutting out, NCEC friezes are ideal for use with children of all ages. As well as making traditional friezes, most of the material can be used to make 3-dimensional scenes. Based on a variety of themes:

Palm Sunday and Easter	*A Christmas Frieze*
The Christmas Story	*Harvest*
People of the World	*Feed the World*
Ministry of Jesus	*Stories Jesus Told*
The Early Church	*Make-it-yourself Bible Chart*